# Next Gen PET Development Team

## Co-authors of Next Gen PET

Fred Goldberg, San Diego State University
Stephen Robinson, Tennessee Technological University
Danielle Harlow, University of California at Santa Barbara
Julie Andrew, University of Colorado at Boulder
Edward Price, California State University at San Marcos
Michael McKean, San Diego State University

## Contributed to Development of Materials

Valerie Otero, University of Colorado at Boulder
Paula Engelhardt, Tennessee Technological University
Rebecca Stober, University of Colorado at Boulder
Cary Sneider, Portland State University
Rebecca Kruse Vincent, National Science Foundation
Nephi Thompson, Colorado Mountain College
David Mitchell, California Polytechnic University at San Luis Obispo
Leslie Atkins, Boise State University

## Field Test Collaborators

David Mitchell, California Polytechnic University at San Luis Obispo
Anne Marie Bergen, California Polytechnic University at San Luis Obispo
Lola Berber-Jimenez, California Polytechnic University at San Luis Obispo
Nancy Stauch, California Polytechnic University at San Luis Obispo
Tina Duran, California Polytechnic University at San Luis Obispo
Chance Hoellwarth, California Polytechnic University at San Luis Obispo
Paula Engelhardt, Tennessee Technological University

## Technical Support

Shawn Alff, San Diego State University
Katie Badham, San Diego State University
Megan Santos, San Diego State University
James Powell, San Diego State University
Anne E. Leak, University of California at Santa Barbara
Noreen Balos, University of California at Santa Barbara
Leo Farias, California Polytechnic University at San Luis Obispo
Loren Johnson, California Polytechnic University at San Luis Obispo
Liz Walker, Tennessee Technological University
Ryan Calloway, Tennessee Technological University
Carla Moore, Tennessee Technological University
Ian Robinson, Tennessee Technological University
Rob Reab, Tennessee Technological University
Nate Reynolds, California State University San Marcos
Lauran Gerhart, California State University San Marcos

# Next Generation Physical Science and Everyday Thinking
# Magnetism and Static Electricity
# Lecture-style Class

*Each unit is separately paginated.*

---

[1] Extensions (Ext) are online, interactive homework activities.

# Next Generation Physical Science and Everyday Thinking

## Magnetism and Static Electricity
### *Lecture-style Class*

YOUR PARTNER IN STEM EDUCATION

YOUR PARTNER IN STEM EDUCATION

333 North Bedford Road
Mount Kisco, NY 10549
Phone (914) 273-2233
Fax (914) 206-6444
www.iat.com

*Next Generation Physical Science and Everyday Thinking* (*Next Gen PET*)
© 2017 San Diego State University Research Foundation
Licensed exclusively to It's About Time.

Printed and bound in the United States of America.

ISBN 978-1-68231-289-6
**Pre-Publication**
1 2 3 4 5    21 20 19 18 17

Major support for the development of *Next Gen PET* came from the National Science Foundation Grant No. 1044172 and the Chevron Corporation. Opinions expressed are those of the authors and not necessarily those of the National Science Foundation.

human energy

# Unit M
# Developing a Model for Magnetism

**Lecture-style Class**

# Unit M: Developing a Model for Magnetism
## Table of Contents

---

[1] Extensions (Ext's) are online, interactive homework activities.

## Purpose

When scientists try to explain what they see happening in the world around them, they construct models to help them understand why things happen as they do. In general, a scientific model is a set of connected ideas that can be used to explain phenomena that have already been observed and also guide the making of predictions about experiments that have yet to be performed. Models can be represented in various ways, such as physical objects, diagrams on a page, written or verbal descriptions, and algebraic relationships (equations). In this course you will encounter and use all of these types of models, but initially you will engage in one of the most important processes of science: that of developing your own models. When developing your own model or evaluating someone else's, it is important to be able to decide whether the model is good or not. We will introduce you to the scientific practice of developing, testing, and revising modeling by using a simple situation: figuring out a model to explain how the mystery tube works.

The key question for this lesson is:

LESSON **?**

*How can you decide whether a model is good or not?*

## Developing a Model for the Mystery Tube

The mystery tube has four strings emerging from four numbered holes. (The knots (or beads) attached to each string are simply to stop the ends from passing into the tube.) Your task in this lesson is to develop a model of how these strings are arranged inside the tube, based only on observations you can make from outside the tube.

However, before you can propose an initial model, you need to have some evidence to base it on. Watch a movie (UM L1 Mov1) of someone pulling the string in the upper right (labeled 2).

 What happens?

Based on this one observation, you can construct your first model for how you think the strings are arranged inside the tube.

 Draw lines on the diagram below to show how you think the strings are arranged inside the tube. Briefly explain why you drew them as you did.

**First Model**

 Use your first model to make a prediction. When string 3 (on lower left) is pulled, what do you expect to happen?

---

**CQ 1-1: When string 3 (on lower left) is pulled, what do you expect to happen?**

A. Nothing.
B. String 3 will get longer, but no other string will be affected.
C. String 3 will get a longer and string 1 will get shorter.
D. String 3 will get longer and string 4 will be pulled tight.
E. Something else will happen.

---

Watch a movie (UM L1 Mov2) of someone pulling string 3.

 What happens?

Did your first model account for your observation?

If it did account for the observations, then at this point you should have a 'good' model, because it can explain the evidence so far (the outcomes of the two observations). However, if your observation did not match your prediction from your first model, then you need to revise your model.

**Second Model**

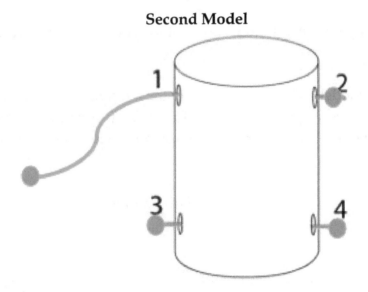

Use your second model to make a prediction. When string 4 (on lower right) is pulled, what do you expect to happen?

**CQ 1-2: When string 4 (on lower right) is pulled, what do you expect to happen?**

A. Nothing.
B. String 4 will get longer, but no other string will be affected.
C. String 4 will get a longer and string 1 will get shorter.
D. String 4 will get longer and string 2 will get shorter.
E. Something else will happen.

Watch a movie (UM L1 Mov3) of someone pulling string 4.

 What happens?

 Did your second model account for your latest observation?

If your model has accounted for all the evidence so far, then at this point you should have a 'good' model. However, if your latest observation did not match your prediction from your second model, then you need to revise your model.

**Third Model**

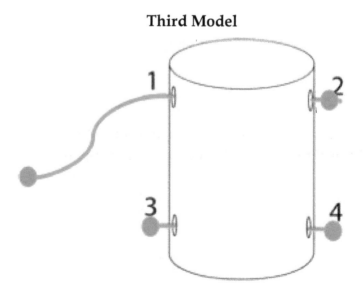

Finally, Watch a movie (UM L1 Mov4) where several strings are pulled.

Record your observations here.

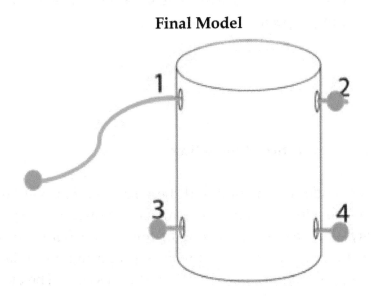 Use the evidence from this last movie to draw your 'final' model for the mystery tube.

**Final Model**

## Summarizing Question

**S1**. Your instructor will show you several different possible models for the mystery tube.

---

**CQ 1-3: Which of the mystery tube models shown by your instructor is closest to the one your group constructed?**

A. Model A
B. Model B
C. Model C
D. Model D
E. Model E

---

**S2**. In general, in science, why is it important to make a prediction before performing a specific experiment?

**The scientific practice of modeling**

In the remainder of this unit and the next one, you will be developing your own models to explain phenomena involving magnetism and static electricity. Just as you practiced in this lesson with the mystery tube, the scientific practice of modeling involves proposing an initial model, testing it by making predictions, and revising it if necessary. The cycle continues until your model can 'explain' a wide range of phenomena of interest and also make accurate predictions for new situations where the model is still applicable. Scientists engage in this practice all the time.

## Purpose and Materials Needed

You are no doubt familiar with some magnetic phenomena, like using a magnet to hold paper on a refrigerator door, or using a compass to navigate. However, could you explain to someone else how these work? In this unit you will first investigate some phenomena involving magnets to establish their basic properties, and then develop a model that can explain your observations and be used to make predictions for new experiments.

## *What are some properties of magnetic interactions?*

Your group's kit has the following materials that you will use for this lesson:

▸ Deep-dish bowl
▸ Disc of Styrofoam
▸ An envelope containing several items (See Table 1 below)
▸ Small magnetic compass
▸ Piece of tape
▸ Empty zippered plastic bag to use to empty the water in at the end of class
▸ In addition, your team should have a bottle of water.

One member in your group should get a **bar magnet** and four small **disc magnets** (or a total of four bar magnets or four of any other type of magnet) from your instructor. Another group member should pick up three nails. Keep the nails far away from the magnets.

> **When you get the magnets, keep them on the floor, far away from the nails and any other items in your kit, until you are directed to use them.**

## Predictions, Observations and Making Sense

### Part 1: How do magnets interact with other materials and with each other?

Do all types of objects show magnetic effects? That is, are all objects attracted to a magnet?

---

**CQ 2-1: What kinds of materials do you think are attracted to a magnet?**

A. All materials, both metals (copper, aluminum, iron, brass, etc.) and non-metals (plastic, wood, glass, etc.)
B. Only metals, but not non-metals
C. Only non-metals, but not metals
D. Only certain metals, not all metals
E. Only certain metals and non-metals, but not all of them

---

To find out, lay the items listed in the table below (from your envelope) on a desktop. [If materials are not available, watch a movie (UM L2 Mov1)] You will also need a plastic pen or plastic ruler. **[Only test one nail. Place other nails far away from the magnet.]** Bring the bar magnet near each. For each item, record in the table whether it is attracted (A) to the magnet, repelled (R) from the magnet, or there is no effect (O). For each case, turn the magnet around and see if you get the same effect, or if something different happens (and if so, record that in the table). Add two other items of your own choice to the table and test them.

### Table I: Observations of Magnet near Objects (A, R or O)

| | Wood strip | Steel paper clip | Plastic pen or ruler | Alumi-num strip | Iron nail | Copper wire | Nickel strip or wire | | |
|---|---|---|---|---|---|---|---|---|---|
| **Magnet** | | | | | | | | | |

Look over the data you recorded in Table I.

 Does a magnet affect all objects? If not, which of the objects does a magnet affect?

---

Does it make any difference which end of the magnet is used?

Steel is an alloy (solid mixture) of iron and carbon[1]. Based on your observations, what kinds of materials seem to be affected by a magnet?

Materials that are either attracted to a magnet or are magnets themselves are called *ferromagnetic materials*. Iron is the most common ferromagnetic material, and objects or materials that include iron in them (like steel) are also ferromagnetic. (Nickel and cobalt are also examples of ferromagnetic materials.)

Take the two small disk (or other types of) magnets in your hands and bring their faces (or ends) together slowly, but try not to let them touch each other.

Describe what you feel as they approach each other.

Now turn **one** of the magnets around and bring them together again.

Do they behave in the same way as before, or do you feel something different? If so, what?

When scientists study the natural world, they focus their attention on different types of interactions between objects. When two objects interact, they *act on* or *influence* each other in some way. In this course, you will be studying many different types of interactions. The interactions you saw above, between two magnets, and also between a magnet and a ferromagnetic material, are examples of what we will call a ***magnetic interaction***.

---

[1] Stainless steel is an alloy of steel and chromium. There are two types, one of which is affected by magnets and the other is not.

You have observed two examples of magnetic interactions. In one example, each end of a magnet interacts with a second magnet. In the other example, each end of a magnet interacts with a ferromagnetic material that is not itself a magnet; e.g., a steel paper clip. How are these two examples of magnetic interactions different from each other?

When you are done, put the items back into the envelope. Place the bar magnet and disc (or other) magnets back on the floor—far away from the other nails.

In the rest of this lesson, you will use iron (steel) nails to explore some important properties of the magnetic interaction.

## Part 2: What happens when a nail is rubbed with a magnet?

In this experiment you will distinguish between two types of nails: those that are rubbed with a magnet (called *rubbed*), and those that are not rubbed with a magnet (called *unrubbed*). Initially all your nails should be *unrubbed*.

> **Please keep the bar magnet far away from the iron nails until you are directed to use it. Once you rub a nail, it is no longer "unrubbed." Please do *not* rub the nails until you are asked to do so.**

Watch the movies **(UM L2 Mov2 and UM L2 Mov3) of how you should carry out the following explorations. It is important that everyone follows the same procedure.** Below are instructions that you may refer to after the movies.

To make a sensitive detector, place the dish on the table with enough water in it to fill it to a depth of about one-half inch. Place the small float in the water and put one of the **unrubbed** nails on it. The nail  may stick out more than the one shown here in the figure. (If it does not float freely, you may need to add a little more water to the dish.)

Now make a **rubbed** nail as follows. Far away from the floating nail, pick up a second **unrubbed** nail and hold it horizontally at its head end. (The end you would hit with a hammer.) Pick up the bar magnet, hold it at right angles to the nail and slide one end of the magnet (either end is OK) **all the way from the head to the point end of the nail**.

Then lift up the bar magnet and repeat this a few more times, always sliding it in the same direction (**not** back and forth).

Record here which Pole of the magnet (N or S) you used to touch and slide across the nail from head to tip: _____

*After you have rubbed the nail, be sure to place the magnet back on the floor.*

You will now investigate how this rubbed nail interacts with the floating unrubbed nail by doing the following. Hold the rubbed nail horizontally in your hand and bring its tip **close to** (but not touching) the floating unrubbed nail.  See the picture to the right showing that the held nail should be **horizontal** (just above and parallel to  the surface of the water) and at **right angles** to the floating nail.

Always test held and floating nails this way.  Do not bring the held nail downward from above (picture below to the left), and do not bring it parallel to the floating nail (picture below to the right).

**Do NOT do it this way (from above)**    **Do NOT do it this way (parallel)**

🔍 What, if anything, happens to the tip of the floating unrubbed nail? Is it attracted (A), repelled R), or does it show no reaction (O)? Record your observation in the appropriate box in Table II below.

🔍 Next, bring the point end of the rubbed nail near the head end of the unrubbed nail and record your observations in Table II.

🔍 Finally, bring the head end of the rubbed nail near the point end of the unrubbed nail, and then bring it near the head end of the unrubbed nail. Record both observations in Table II.

[If appropriate, you can watch a movie (UM L2 Mov4) of these effects.]

**Table II: Interactions between Rubbed and Unrubbed Nails (A, R or O)**

|  | Point end of **unrubbed** nail | Head end of **unrubbed** nail |
|---|---|---|
| Point end of (held) magnet-rubbed nail |  |  |
| Head end of (held) magnet-rubbed nail |  |  |

🧩 Do the two ends of the **unrubbed nail** behave the same way or differently when each end of the magnet-rubbed nail is brought nearby?

Lay the rubbed nail aside for a moment. *Imagine* that you removed the floating nail, rubbed it with the magnet in **exactly the same way** that you rubbed the other nail, and then floated it again. (**DON'T DO IT YET!**) You would then have two rubbed nails — one held and one floating.

❓ Predict what you think would happen if you were to bring the tip of the held **rubbed** nail near the tip of the floating **rubbed** nail.

?🧑 Predict what you think would happen if you were to bring the tip of the held **rubbed** nail hear the head of the floating **rubbed** nail.

Now remove the floating nail, rub it with the magnet using the **same end** of the magnet you used previously, and replace it on the floater. Then test your predictions.

🔍 Repeat the same set of four tests that you did in STEP 3 with the two rubbed nails. Record your observations in Table III below. [If appropriate, you can watch a movie (UM L2 Mov5) of these effects.]

**Table III: Interactions between Two Rubbed Nails (A, R or O)**

|  | Point end of (floating) **magnet-rubbed** nail | Head end of (floating) **magnet-rubbed** nail |
|---|---|---|
| Point end of (held) magnet-rubbed nail |  |  |
| Head end of (held) magnet-rubbed nail |  |  |

🧩 Do the two ends of the magnet-rubbed floating nail behave the same way or differently when each end of the magnet-rubbed nail is brought nearby?

🧩 Based on your observations, would you claim that rubbing a nail in the way you did turned it into a magnet with two ends that behave differently? Yes or no? What evidence supports your answer?

When a nail (or any other object made of a ferromagnetic material) is rubbed with a magnet and behaves in the same way as you observed above, we say it is *magnetized*. Therefore, from now on we will refer to a 'rubbed nail' as a 'magnetized nail,' and an 'unrubbed nail' as an 'unmagnetized nail.'

Some magnetized objects retain their magnetism for very long periods of time, and we call them *permanent magnets*. The bar magnet you are using is probably made from alnico, an alloy of iron with **al**uminum, **ni**ckel and **co**balt, that is a good permanent magnet. Other ferromagnetic materials, which tend to loose their magnetism easily after being magnetized, are sometimes called *temporary magnets*.

Suppose you were to touch a magnetized nail all over with your fingers.

? Do you think the nail would still be magnetized after you did this, or would it act more like an unmagnetized nail now? Why do you think so?

Now test your thinking by touching one of your magnetized nails all over with your fingers. Place it on the float and test its ends with your second magnetized nail.

Was the nail still magnetized after you touched it all over or not?

? Now suppose you dropped a magnetized nail in water. Do you think the nail would still be magnetized after you did this, or not? Why do you think so?

Again, test your thinking by dropping one of your magnetized nails in your pan of water. Then place it on the float and test its ends with another magnetized nail.

Was the nail still magnetized after it was immersed in water, or not?

Your instructor will review the observations with the class. If appropriate, you can watch a movie (UM L2 Mov6) of the effects.

## Part 3: How are the ends of magnets and magnetized objects labeled?

Place a **magnetized** nail on the floater, making sure the other rubbed nail and the bar magnet are far away. [If your chair or table has steel legs or supports, they may affect the following observation. In that case, you should try to keep the dish away from the steel by moving it to a different part of the chair top or table, or just holding the dish in the air.] Now do the following a few times. (You may have to wait up to a half a minute or so each time for the nail to settle into a stable position.)

- Aim the floating nail in different directions in the middle of the pan, then release it and wait until it settles into a stable position. (Make sure the floater does not get 'stuck' against the side of the pan while this is happening.)

- Spin the floating rubbed nail gently, and again wait until it settles into a stable position.

Your instructor will point out the approximate directions for north, south, east and west. You can watch a movie (UM L2 Mov7) of the effect if materials are not available.

 Does the floating magnetized nail end up pointing in a different direction each time, or does it always seem to end up pointing in the same direction? If so, in which direction does the pointed end of the nail seem to 'want' to point?

---

**CQ 2-2: Which direction is the point end of your group's magnet-rubbed nail pointing after it settles down?**

A. North
B. East
C. South
D. West

---

Whenever a rubbed nail, or any magnet, is allowed to rotate freely, without another magnet nearby, one end will always end up pointing (approximately) towards the geographical North Pole of the Earth. By mutual agreement, scientists **define** this end of the magnet as the *north-seeking pole* (or N-pole for short) of the magnet. The opposite end of the magnet, by definition, is called the *south-seeking pole* (S-pole). (Your bar magnet may already have its ends labeled as N and S to signify this.) Thus, when you rub your nail you turn it into a magnet with a N-pole and a S-pole.

Is the tip (pointed) end of your group's floating magnetized nail a N-pole or a S-pole? What about the head end?

In your kit, you should also have a small magnetic compass. Take it out and place it on the palm of your hand, holding it far away from the magnet and the magnet-rubbed nails. The needle in the compass is made of a special ferromagnetic material that has been magnetized and retains its properties for a long time; i.e., it is a small permanent magnet.

The compass needle is free to pivot, and so one end of the needle will always point towards geographic north—and by definition, that is the N-pole of the compass needle. (Notice that, in effect, your floating magnetized nail is also a compass needle.)

Which end of **your** compass needle is a N-pole, the colored tip or the uncolored tip? (Do not rely on the labels on the compass itself. Instead, use the directions above to help you. Other groups' compasses may be different from yours.)

## Part 4: How do the poles of two magnets interact with each other?

Lay your compass on the table and rotate it so that the N-pole end of the compass needle is aligned with the "N" marking (for the North direction) on the casing of the compass (as in the picture above).

Lay one of your magnetized nails on the table with its N-pole pointing towards the "E" (for East) label on the compass, and then slide it towards the compass, as shown in the picture below. [*Note: Your magnetized nail may have its N-pole at its head end, in which case you would slide its head end toward the compass.*]

Magnetized nail

What happens to the N-pole of the compass needle? Is it attracted to or repelled by the N-pole of the nail?

Move your magnetized nail away from the compass and turn it around so that its S-pole faces the E-label of the compass. Now slide it towards the compass again.

What happens to the N-pole of the compass needle now? What about the S-pole of the compass needle?

Do like poles (N-N or S-S) of the magnetized nail and compass needle attract or repel each other? Do unlike poles (N-S, or S-N) attract or repel each other?

Check your conclusions with at least one other group to make sure you all agree. If not, repeat the observations. If appropriate, you can watch a movie (UM L2 Mov8) of the effects.

Your statement about how like and unlike Poles interact with each other is known as the *Law of Magnetic Poles*.

As you have seen in this lesson, the two ends of a magnetized nail behave differently when near another magnetized nail. Because of this property, we say that a magnetized nail is '*two-ended*.' On the other hand, since both ends of the unmagnetized nail behave the same when near another magnetized nail, we say that it is '*one-ended*.'

## Summarizing Questions

**S1:** An elementary school student asks you for advice about a science project she is doing on recycling. She suggests that a large permanent magnet could be used to separate metals from non-metals in the trash passing through a recycling station. What do you think of this idea?

**S2.** In this lesson you magnetized a nail by rubbing its surface with a magnet. Do you think that whatever causes a nail to be magnetic also lies on its surface, or inside the nail? What evidence supports your thinking?

## Purpose

In the previous lesson you discovered that magnet-rubbed (magnetized) iron nails behave differently from unrubbed (unmagnetized) iron nails. Thus, rubbing the nail with a magnet must change the nail in some way. But *how* does it change the nail? To answer this question, you need to develop a model—a picture and description of what you think is going on inside the nail.

In Lesson 1 you developed a model for the Mystery Tube. Scientists construct models all the time to help them understand new phenomena. As you saw in Lesson 1, a good model can do two important things: (1) it can be used to **explain** observations from experiments already done; and (2) it can guide the making of **predictions** about experiments that have not yet been done. After scientists make their predictions based on their model, they (or other scientists) perform the experiments. If the predictions are **confirmed** through the new experiments, the scientists retain their model because it can explain their new observations. However, if the results of the new experiments differ from the predictions, scientists use the new evidence to **revise** their model so it can explain the new set of observations (as well as the previous observations). Then they use their revised model to make new predictions. They develop confidence in their model only after it can be used repeatedly to make predictions that are confirmed in new experiments. A critically important activity of scientists is to develop, test, and revise models.

 *How can you develop a model for magnetism?*

# Predictions, Observations and Making Sense

## Part 1: What is your initial model for magnetism?

A **good model** in science meets the following criteria:

- The model (the drawing and the written part) should be clear and understandable. If you use 'symbols' in your drawing of a model, you should describe in words what the nature of those symbols are; that is, what they represent.
- The model should be plausible and causal; that is, it should make sense according to your own ideas about cause and effect. In the case of a model for magnetism, what you show happening when a nail is rubbed with a magnet should both make sense and explicitly indicate how moving the magnet along the surface of the nail causes something to happen in or on the nail.
- The model should account for (explain) all the observable evidence and not contradict any of that evidence.
- The model should guide accurate predictions about what would happen in new experiments.

You know from previous observations that a magnet rubbed nail becomes magnetized and is *two-ended*. Imagine that you rub the unrubbed nail in such a way that its point end becomes a North Pole. [You can always test this using the compass.] Below are two drawings of the nail, representing its state before and after rubbing with a magnet.

?  **Individually**, sketch what you think might be different about the iron nail in these two conditions (unmagnetized and magnetized). Think about what entities might be inside the nail, and what might happen to them in the process of rubbing with a magnet, that causes the nail to become magnetized and two-ended. Use symbols like + and -, N and S, or some combination of them to represent the entities. Do not use abstract symbols, like arrows or rectangles, since it would be difficult to interpret what they mean. To make things concrete, assume you rubbed the nail so its point is a North Pole and its head is a South Pole.

**Your first <u>individual</u> model:**

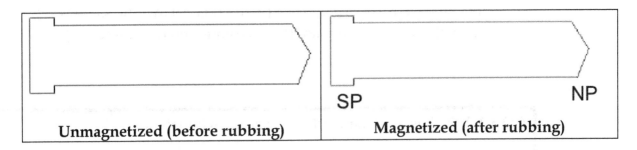

**Unmagnetized (before rubbing)** | **Magnetized (after rubbing)**

Describe <u>your</u> initial *model* in words, in particular how the "Magnetized" picture differs from the "Unmagnetized" picture, and how rubbing with a magnet causes this difference. Describe what you imagine the entities inside the nail represent. Your picture and written description is a representation of your own initial model for explaining what happens when a nail is magnetized.

Each member of your group should now describe her initial model to the other group members by carefully describing what the entities are and how they become rearranged in some way (if at all) when the nail is magnetized. Then try to decide on one model that represents the group's 'best' thinking.

Sketch your **group's best initial model**.

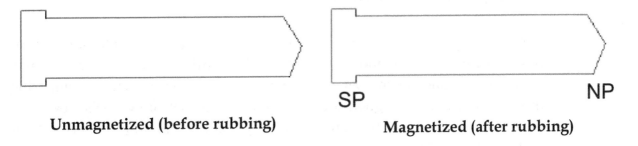

**Unmagnetized (before rubbing)**    **Magnetized (after rubbing)**

Discuss within your group how the model can 'explain' why rubbing an unmagnetized nail with a magnet results in it becoming *magnetized*.

Discuss within your group how the model represents that an unmagnetized nail is *one-ended* (both ends behave the same way), but a magnetized nail is *two-ended* (the two ends behave differently).

---

**CQ 3-1**: Which is most similar to your group's initial model?

A. Plus (+) and minus (-) entities are randomly spread throughout the unrubbed nail; rubbing separates them to the two halves of the nail.
B. North (N) and South (S) entities are randomly spread throughout the unrubbed nail; rubbing separates them to the two halves of the nail
C. Some other type of entities are inside the nail; rubbing causes them to re-orient or change in some other way than being separated to the two halves of the nail.
D. Something different from above

---

In the past we have found that most groups at this point suggest a model that has the following features. Inside the unrubbed nail there are two different types of entities, either plusses and minuses or norths and souths, and the individual entities are scattered randomly throughout the nail. During the act of sliding the magnet across the nail, the two types of entities separate from each other: one type goes towards one end, and the other type goes towards the other end. Because this initial model is so common, we give it its own name: the *separation model*.

For groups that have invented some form of a separation model, some groups have probably used + and – symbols as the entities, and other groups may have used N and S symbols as the entities. For consistency in comparing models, it would be a good idea to agree on one set of symbols. Batteries have + and - labels at their ends, and magnets have N and S labels at their ends (poles). Since we are focusing on magnetic effects here, not electric effects, to keep things simple, we suggest everyone uses N and S labels in their model (if appropriate).

Re-draw your group's initial model, **using N and S labels** for the entities (if appropriate). You might also decide to adopt a different model from your original one, and that's fine; just draw it below.

---

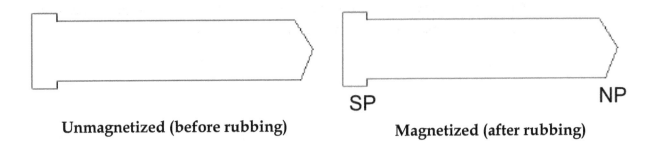

Unmagnetized (before rubbing)          Magnetized (after rubbing)

## Part 2: Testing the initial model

In Part 1, you developed a model that you believe best explains some observations you have already made. The model should have been clear and understandable, plausible and causal, and explanatory, as described at the beginning of Part 1. The other important criterion of a good model is that it is predictive; that is, it leads to accurate predictions about the outcomes of new experiments. You will be testing that criterion in this part of the lesson.

> Important: When you make predictions, you must base them on your current model. Do not change your model as a result of just thinking about the situation, because then you are not testing your model. If the outcome of the experiment turns out to be exactly what you had predicted, then don't modify your model. On the other hand, if the outcome is different from your prediction, even in small ways, then you need to consider how to revise your model. Finally, for this process to be useful, the predictions you make should be precise, not vague and general. Only then will the experiment really test your model appropriately.

To help your group make a prediction based on its initial model (rather than on some other intuition), you should use the following procedure. On a separate piece of paper draw a large version of your current model for a **magnetized nail**. Next draw a thick vertical line through the exact middle of your model drawing, and then tear your drawing in half, exactly along that line. You should end up with two drawings, each representing half of the magnetized nail. Separate these two halves on your table.

Copy your drawings of the two halves of the model below, showing your model's representation of the two halves of the nail.

**Head half of magnetized nail**          **Point half of magnetized nail**

Now look at the entities inside each half piece and answer these questions **based on your model drawing**.

 Does your model of the **head half piece** (on the left) suggest that it, **by itself,** is one-ended, two-ended, or something different? (One-ended means that the entities are the same on each end, suggesting each end would behave the same. If you think something different, try to describe it in words.)

 Does your model of the **point half piece** (on the right) suggest that it, **by itself,** is one-ended, two-ended, or something different? (If different, try to describe it in words.)

Your drawings above represent what your model suggests would be in each piece of a magnetized nail that is cut in half. You will now use these to make a **prediction** about what you would find if you actually did this and tested each piece of the cut nail separately.

**CQ 3-2.** What does your torn-in-half model drawing predict would happen if the actual rubbed nail were cut in half? [Assume that the act of cutting does not rearrange the entities in any way. They stay where they were before cutting.]

A. The head half piece would now be one-ended, and the point half piece would also be one-ended (but with opposite types of entities).
B. The head half piece would now be two-ended, and the point half piece would also be two-ended (each piece has different kinds of entities at each end).
C. One half piece would be one-ended and the other half piece would be neither one-ended nor two-ended.
D. Neither half piece would be one-ended or two-ended.
E. Something else would happen

Watch a movie (**UM L3 Mov1**) from which you can determine whether your prediction was accurate or not. In the movie, the person first magnetizes the nail by rubbing it with a bar magnet. He then brings first the tip of the rubbed nail, and then the head of the rubbed nail, near the E-label on the compass.

What does the compass needle do in each case?

Is the point end of the rubbed nail a North Pole or a South Pole?

Do the observations suggest that the rubbed nail is two-ended, one-ended, or something else?

Next the person carefully cuts the nail exactly in half. He will now test each half piece.

What happens when he brings each end of the head half piece near the E-label on the compass?

Do the observations suggest that the head half piece is two-ended, one-ended, or something else?

What happens when he brings each end of the point half piece near the E-label on the compass?

Do the observations suggest that the point half piece is two-ended, one-ended, or something else?

What can you conclude from this experiment?

---

**CQ 3-3**: When a rubbed nail is cut in half, what can you conclude?

A. Each half piece is still two-ended.
B. Each half piece is one-ended.
C. One half piece is one-ended, and the other is two-ended.
D. Conclude something else. [Describe what.]

---

Your group used its initial model to make a prediction about what would happen if the rubbed nail were cut in half. If what actually happened differs from your prediction, then your group needs to revise its initial model.

Does your group's initial model need to be revised: yes or no?

If you answered 'yes,' before you revise it we want to provide you with some additional evidence to guide you.

Watch the following movie (UM L3 Mov2). The person starts, as before, by magnetizing the nail so its point end is a North Pole. The person will now cut the rubbed nail into two **unequal** pieces, one longer, one shorter. He'll then bring each end of each piece near the E-label on the compass.

What happens when each end of the *longer piece* is brought near the E-label on the compass?

Do the observations suggest that the longer piece is two-ended, one-ended, or something else?

What happens when each end of the shorter piece is brought near the E-label on the compass?

Do the observations suggest that the shorter piece is two-ended, one-ended, or something else?

What can you conclude from this experiment? When a rubbed nail is cut in unequal length pieces, is each piece still two-ended, one-ended, or something else (describe)?

The person in the movie could have cut the rubbed nail *anywhere* along its length. In each case, however, you would have concluded that each cut piece is two-ended.

Your group now needs to be creative and revise your initial model so it could account for <u>all</u> the new evidence.

**Your group's revised model:**

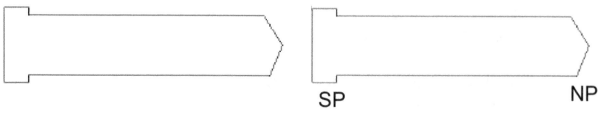

**Unmagnetized (before rubbing)**     **Magnetized (after rubbing)**

How does your revised model account for the observation that cutting a magnetized nail **anywhere along its length** would still give two pieces that are both *two-ended*? (If it cannot account for this, say why not.)

One member of your group should take a picture of the group's revised model with a cellphone camera and e-mail it according to your instructor's directions. On the subject line, type "Group N **revised** model," where N represents your group number.

## Summarizing Question

---

**CQ 3-4**. Can <u>your</u> group's revised model explain the observation that cutting the magnetized nail anywhere along its length will produce two pieces that are each magnetized (two-ended)?

A. Yes, it can.
B. No, it cannot.
C. We are not sure.

---

Your instructor may share some of the class' revised models. You may wish to copy down some of these other models if you think they will be helpful.

## Purpose and Materials Needed

In the previous lesson your group created an initial model for magnetism that could explain the two-endedness property of magnetized nails. Then you used the model to make a prediction. Most likely, the experimental results were not what you had predicted and you needed to revise your model. By the end of the lesson, you realized that a successful model must account for the observation that cutting a magnetized (two-ended) nail *anywhere* along its length would produce two pieces that are each magnetized. Many groups, however, may not have been able to create a revised model that was completely satisfactory.

When this happens in science, it is often the case that scientists need to radically reconceptualize their model. For example, in the case of the model for magnetism, perhaps you need to think differently about what kinds of entities are inside the nail. Thinking in terms of separate N and S entities might not be fruitful. In this lesson you will gather evidence that could help you reconceptualize your model of magnetism; that is, help you think again about what kinds of entities might be inside of a nail, and what happens to them when the nail is rubbed with a magnet.

*How can you develop a better model for magnetism?*

## Predictions, Observations and Making Sense

### Part 1: Thinking about the effects of collections of magnets or magnetized nails

A magnetized nail can interact with an unmagnetized nail (attracting each end), but an unmagnetized nail does not interact with another unmagnetized nail (there are no effects). This suggests that whatever entities are inside the nail, in an unmagnetized nail these entities collectively produce no magnetic effects outside the nail. On the other hand, rubbing the nail causes something to happen to these entities so that collectively they do produce magnetic effects outside the nail.

From the last lesson you can infer that the entities inside the nail cannot be separate N and S entities that rearrange themselves when the nail is rubbed, because that kind of model cannot explain all the observations. So perhaps the *entities* need to be something *different*. The following movies will provide evidence that could help you re-think about what the entities might be, and how they might behave when the nail is magnetized.

To begin, watch a movie (UM L4 Mov1) of a compass with its north pole pointing towards the N-label on the compass housing. This is the zero degree mark. Previously, you had seen that a single magnetized nail placed near the E-label on the compass housing could cause the compass needle to deflect. In this movie, the person rubs four nails identically to magnetize them the same, and places them close to the E-label on the compass housing. The needle should rotate, suggesting that the combination of four magnetized nails produce a significant magnetic effect.

Arrow faces north

 Are the point ends of the four nails North Poles or a South Poles? How do you know?

Do four magnetized nails all arranged the same way produce a larger, smaller, or about the same rotation of the compass needle as a single magnetized nail?

The four nails have their N-poles all aligned, pointing in the same direction, and the combination produces a magnetic effect in the area away from the nails (causing the compass needle to rotate). Does the orientation of the poles make any difference? What would happen if two of the nails were turned around, so their N-poles pointed in the opposite direction to the other two nails?

---

**CQ 4-1:** Imagine you turned two of the nails around, so their South Poles faced the compass. The other two nails had their North Poles facing the compass. What do you predict would happen to the compass needle?

    A. It would stay the same, neither rotating more nor less.
    B. It would rotate more.
    C. It would rotate less, or not at all

---

 Why do you think so?

Watch the movie **(UM L4 Mov2)** of what happens.

 Describe what happens.

Can a combination of four magnetized nails cancel out (or almost cancel out) each other's effect? If so, under what conditions would that happen?

In the next movie **(UM L4 Mov3)**, the experimenter grabs ten bar magnets and arranges them so all the North Poles are pointing in the same direction. He then lowers the collection of magnets into a pile of paper clips.

Describe what happens.

> **CQ 4-2.** Imagine the person changed the orientation of half the bar magnets, so half had their North Poles pointing one way and the other half had their North Poles pointing the other way, and then lowered this new collection of bar magnets into a different pile of paper clips. Would the combination of ten magnets pick up about the same number of paper clips, many more, or many fewer or none at all?
>
> A. About the same number
> B. Many more
> C. Many fewer, or none at all

 Why do you think so?

Watch the movie (UM L4 Mov4) of what happens.

Describe what happens.

Next, watch a movie (UM L4 Mov5) of a computer simulation that models what happens when small magnets are oriented different ways. The simulation uses a meter that measures how strongly the combination of magnets would influence a nearby compass needle (or another magnet) placed where the meter is located. Pay attention to what happens to the meter reading as more magnets are added, with their poles all aligned.

Record the value of the meter readings in the different arrangements.

Next, watch the movie (UM L4 Mov6) of what happens when the orientation of the magnets are changed so their north poles point in random directions.

As more magnets are added in combination, with their poles all pointing in the same direction, does the strength of the magnetic effect increase, decrease, or remain about the same?

If several magnets in a group have their poles oriented in *random directions*, does that arrangement produce a stronger magnetic effect or a weaker magnetic effect than if the magnets were all oriented in the same direction?

What can you conclude from this? Fill in the following:

*So, a group of magnets can collectively produce a large magnetic effect or little or no magnetic effect, depending on how the magnets are oriented with respect to each other. If their North Poles all point in the same (or nearly the same) direction, there would be _____ magnetic effect. On the other hand, if their North Poles point in all different directions (i.e. randomly oriented), there would be* _____ *magnetic effect.*

So, assuming you start with a bunch of magnets with their North Poles randomly oriented, how could you change their orientation to make them all aligned? We'll explore that in the next part of this lesson.

## Part 2: Changing the orientation of magnets

In the previous part, you concluded that if you have several magnets, the combination could produce either a large magnetic effect or a little or no magnetic effect, depending on the relative orientations of the magnet poles. So, if you have a combination of magnets with their poles randomly oriented, what might you do to cause all the poles of the magnets to align? To start simple, consider just a single magnet.

Imagine you have a magnet that is fixed in position and can only pivot (rotate) around its center. What do you think would happen to the pivoting magnet if another magnet were dragged above it from left to right, as shown in the picture below?

Watch the movie (UM L4 Mov7) of this situation.

Describe what happens to the magnet on the pivot as the South Pole of the other magnet is dragged from left to right.

Which end of the magnet on the pivot is its North Pole: the end with the small dot or the end without the small dot? How do you know?

Of course, if we started with a collection of many magnets, each free to rotate about its own pivot, then we could change the orientation of all the magnets by dragging a magnet across the collection.

## Part 3: A final model for magnetism

Hopefully, your investigations in Parts 1 and 2 of this lesson gave you new insight into what you could imagine might be the entities inside a nail, and what would happen to them when you drag a magnet along the nail from one end to the other, thereby magnetizing the nail. Discuss this with your group and draw your group's final model for what you think the entities inside a nail might be and what happens to them when the nail is rubbed from head to tip with the South Pole of a magnet. Remember, your model needs to be able to 'explain' several critical observations:

- *An unrubbed nail produces no magnetic effects (it's unmagnetized).*
- *A rubbed nail is magnetized, producing a large magnetic effect.*
- *A rubbed (magnetized) nail is two ended; that is, each end behaves differently.*
- *A magnetized nail cut anywhere along its length produces two nail pieces that are each magnetized, but each piece produces a weaker magnetic effect than the whole nail.*

**Your group's final model:**

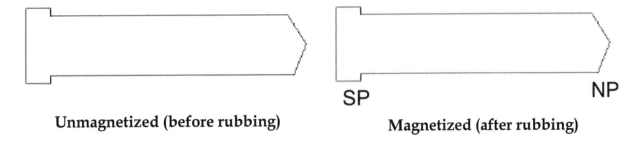

SP                                            NP

**Unmagnetized (before rubbing)**    **Magnetized (after rubbing)**

One member of your group should take a picture of your group's final model and e-mail it according to your instructor's directions. On the subject line, type "Group N final model," where N is your group number.

Your group should spend a few minutes going over each of the four bullet points above and discussing how your group's model can "explain" each of them.

## Summarizing Question

Your instructor will help the class develop a **consensus final model** that is supported by all the evidence collected so far, and that everyone could use to explain magnetic phenomena.

## Purpose and Key Question

By the end of Lesson 4, the class reached consensus on a model of magnetism that could explain all the observations that have been made thus far. We refer to this model as an *alignment model*, and we list its basic features here. (1) Inside ferromagnetic materials, there are a large number of entities that behave *like* tiny magnets. (2) In an unmagnetized ferromagnetic material, the tiny magnets are randomly oriented; that is, just as many magnets have their North Poles pointing in one direction as there are magnets with their South Poles pointing in the same direction. The magnetic effect that each magnet would produce by itself is cancelled by the magnetic effect of a nearby oppositely pointing magnet; thus the entire material produces no magnetic effects. (3) When, for example, the South Pole of a permanent magnet slides across the ferromagnetic material, it attracts the North Poles of every tiny magnet (and repels the South Poles), causing each tiny magnet to pivot (rotate) in place so that all the North Poles end up pointing in the same direction; that is, all the tiny magnets become aligned. In this case, the magnetic effects due to all of the magnets reinforce each other. Thus, the entire material produces a large magnetic effect. It is also assumed that materials that do not exhibit magnetic effects do not contain these tiny magnets.

In this lesson, we will apply the alignment model to make some predictions and to explain some new observations. Remember, a *good* model can do both.

---

LESSON ?

*How can you use the alignment model of magnetism to explain some phenomena?*

---

Your team will need the following:
▶ Several iron nails (at least four)
▶ Paper clips
▶ Small magnetic compass
▶ Small bar magnet (keep far away from everything else)

---

## Predictions, Observations and Making Sense

### Part 1: How can you rub a nail to ensure a particular end is a North Pole?

Based on the alignment model, **predict two different ways** that you could rub a nail with a magnet so that the point end of the nail becomes a North Pole. Discuss with your group and write your predictions below. Briefly indicate your reasoning. [You can use either end of the bar magnet to do the rubbing, and you can rub the nail either direction, from head to point or the other way.]

**After** making your two predictions, try it! Use your compass and apply the Law of Magnetic Poles to check if your nail tip is indeed a North Pole for each case. Record your observations below. You should draw pictures showing which direction you rub the nail, and which end of the magnet you are using.

Consider the following four different ways you might rub the nail:

I. Rub the North end of the magnet from the head to the point end of the nail.

II. Rub the North end of the magnet from the point to the head end of the nail.

III. Rub the South end of the magnet from the head to the point end of the nail.

IV. Rub the South end of the magnet from the point to the head end of the nail.

**CQ 5-1.** Which of the above procedures will produce a magnetized nail with its point end a North Pole?

A. I and II
B. I and III
C. I and IV
D. II and III
E. II and IV

If appropriate, you can watch a movie (UM L5 Mov1) of the various ways you can rub a nail so one end is a particular pole.

## Part 2: Can you magnetize a nail without touching it?

In the previous part, you discovered that rubbing a nail from tip to head with the N-pole of a bar magnet will magnetize the nail, with its point end being a N-pole and its head end being a S-pole. But suppose, instead of sliding the N-pole of the magnet across the nail, you just held its North Pole <u>near</u> the tip of the nail?

**Unrubbed nail**

**CQ 5-2:** If you hold the N-pole of a bar magnet **near** the tip of an unmagnetized (unrubbed) nail, without touching it, what do you think will happen to the nail?

A. It would remain unrubbed; that is, it would not be magnetized.
B. It would be magnetized with the tip a N-pole and the head a S-pole.
C. It would be magnetized with the tip a S-pole and the head a N-pole.
D. Its tip would act like a N-pole, but its head would not have a Pole.
E. Its tip would act like a S-pole, but its head would not have a Pole.

Explain your reasoning.

To test your prediction, lay the compass on the desktop. Then hold an *unmagnetized* (unrubbed) nail on the table with its tip pointed towards the E-label on a compass, as shown below. The tip should be very close to the compass, but not touching it. The compass needle should *not* rotate, indicating the nail is unmagnetized. [If it does rotate, get another and try again.]

Unmagnetized nail

Next, remove the compass and hold the tip of the nail about 0.5 cm from the N-pole of a magnet for a few seconds. *Be sure to hold both the nail and the magnet so they don't move towards each other and touch. If they do touch, start over with another unrubbed nail.* See picture.

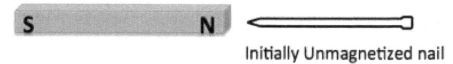

Initially Unmagnetized nail

Then place the nail near the compass again as shown above.

🔍 What happens to the compass needle?

Turn the nail around so its head end is near the E-label on the compass.

🔍 Now what happens to the compass needle?

🧩 What do these two observations suggest happened to the nail? Is it magnetized, with both a N-pole and a S-pole? If so, which end is its N-pole and which end is its S-pole?

If appropriate, you can watch a movie (UM L5 Mov2) of this effect.

Next hold the point end of the **same** (now magnetized) nail about 0.5 cm from the **South Pole** of the bar magnet for a few seconds.

**Already magnetized nail**

Then bring the point end of the nail near the E-label of the compass.

🔍 What happens to the compass needle?

🔍 Turn the nail around and bring its head end near the E-label on the compass. Now what happens to the compass needle?

🧩 Is the nail magnetized? If so, is its point end a North Pole or a South Pole? What about its head end?

🧩 Do these results suggest that a nail can be magnetized without touching a magnet?

🧩 Can a magnetized nail with certain poles have its poles easily switched?

Recall that some ferromagnetic materials (e.g., steel, which is an alloy containing iron) can be easily magnetized and can easily have their poles reversed (as you saw above with the nails). It is also relatively easy to demagnetize them. Such materials, when magnetized, are known as *temporary magnets*. A magnetized nail is an example of a temporary magnet. Certain other kinds of ferromagnetic materials (e.g., Alnico) can be made into *permanent magnets*. These materials are difficult to magnetize, but once magnetized, they are difficult to demagnetize and they retain their pole orientation for a very long time. Bar magnets and compass needles are examples of permanent magnets.

In the following diagram, use the alignment model to explain why the nail becomes magnetized when held near a magnet. First draw the entities inside the unmagnetized nail (top nail), and then draw what happens to them when the nail is near the magnet (bottom nail).

 What caused the entities to re-orient themselves? Be specific and make use of the Law of Magnetic Poles.

## Part 3: Why does a magnet attract unmagnetized (ferromagnetic) objects?

Remember from Lesson 2 that you observed either end of the magnet attracted a paper clip. Watch a movie (UM L5 Mov3) of this effect.

What happens to the paper clip?

Explain why this happens by drawing a set of diagrams (the paper clip before and after the magnet is held nearby), and then writing a few sentences. [Hint: You can think of the paper clip as being similar to an unmagnetized nail.]

In a similar way you can explain why refrigerator magnets stick to steel refrigerators (steel contains iron), or how the Etch-A-Sketch toys work (a magnet attracts tiny particles of iron).

---

**CQ 5-3**. Suppose you bring a magnet near an object and you observe that the object is attracted towards the magnet. What can you conclude about the properties of the object from this <u>one</u> observation?

A. The object is ferromagnetic and was already magnetized before the magnet was brought near.
B. The object is ferromagnetic but was not magnetized before the magnet was brought near.
C. Either A or B could have been true.
D. The object is not ferromagnetic.
E. You cannot conclude anything from this one observation.

---

## Part 4: What happens when you heat a magnetized object?

Imagine you rubbed an iron nail with a bar magnet, and then brought it near the E-label on a compass. You observed the compass needle had rotated a certain amount.

---

**CQ 5-4: Suppose you then heated the magnetized nail with a very hot torch for several seconds. After the nail cooled some, what would you observe the compass needle do if you then brought it near the E-label of the compass?**

    A. It would rotate the same amount as it did before it was heated.
    B. It would rotate much more than it did before it was heated.
    C. It would rotate much less than it did before it was heated.

---

Why do you think so?

 Watch a movie (UM L5 Mov4). Describe what happens.

In terms of the alignment model, what do you think happened to the tiny magnets when the nail was heated?

## Is the U.S. Losing Its Edge? An Engineering Design Challenge

**Maglev train in Japan** (Image Courtesy of Yosemite, GNU Free Documentation License.)

The maglev train has long been the holy grail of ground transportation. Levitating above steel rails, maglev trains need no wheels and have no friction with the track, resulting in an ultra-fast and ultra-quiet ride. So far they're also very expensive. Counting a planned Tokyo-to-Osaka leg, the Japanese maglev project is expected to cost upwards of $100 billion. If that sounds prohibitive, consider that the United States spends significantly more than that on highways in a single year. And while a highway might get you from Los Angeles to San Francisco in six hours if you're lucky, a maglev train like the one Japan's building could theoretically do it in an hour and 15 minutes. In fact, California has been trying to build a Los Angeles-to-San Francisco high-speed rail line for some 30 years, but the fight for funding has been tooth-and-nail. The state is now slated to have a 220-mph train up and running by 2028—but that's just a conventional bullet train, the kind Japan has had for decades. There were once plans for a California-Nevada maglev train, but they never left the station, and the money for planning them ended up being reallocated to a highway project. (*Future Tense*, November 30, 2012[1])

---

[1] By Will Oremus (2012). Why can't we have a 300-MPH floating train like Japan? Future Tense: The Citizens Guide to the Future. *Retrieved from:*
http://www.slate.com/blogs/future_tense/2012/11/30/japan_s_300_mph_maglev_train_why_can_t_the_us_build_high_speed_rail.html.

Although it's true that the U.S. is falling behind other countries in technological accomplishments, a renewed focus on engineering as a part of science education could make a difference, at least in the next generation (which is why the new standards are called the Next Generation Science Standards[2]).

**Beginning to use the engineering design process to design a solution to a problem**

The engineering design process in the Next Generation Science Standards involves three stages: (1) Defining and delimiting an engineering problem (or challenge); (2) Developing possible solutions; (3) Optimizing the design solution. In this initial engineering design lesson we will define and delimit the engineering problem for you and you will sketch out just one possible solution, so you will not need to consider optimizing the solution. Finally, you will also be asked to use your understanding of magnetism to address some issues regarding an actual maglev train.

Your engineering problem is to sketch out the design of a simple system where an object can move a certain distance while floating above the surface. The system will represent a simple model of the maglev train. The object will be a small box that represents the train. The object will move inside a long box from one end to the other (following a gentle push) without touching the bottom (that is, it floats above the bottom of the box). The bottom of the box represents the train tracks.

1. You will need to include magnets in your solution, so you go into a store that sells a wide variety of magnets. You are looking for strips of magnetic material that you can lay along the bottom of the box that you might use in your design of the model. The sales person gives you two choices. Which do you choose and why?

---

[2] NGSS Lead States (2013). *Next Generation Science Standards: Practices, Core Ideas, and Crosscutting Concepts.* Washington, DC: National Academy Press.

a. Strips that are magnetized so the top surface is one pole and the bottom surface is the other pole. (Below is a side view.)

## N (Top)

## S (Bottom)

OR

b. Strips that are magnetized so that one end is one pole and the other pole is the other end. (Below is a side view.)

S                                                                    N

---

### CQ 6-1. Which type of magnetic strips would you choose?

A. Strips that are magnetized so the top surface is one pole and the bottom surface is a different pole.

B. Strips that are magnetized so that one end is one pole and the other end is a different pole.

C. Both would work equally well

2. Be creative and draw a detailed diagram of a possible model maglev train system, consisting of a long box (representing the tracks), magnets, and a small box representing the 'train.' The 'train' should float above the bottom of the box. When you give the box a gentle push, it should move from one end of the box to the other without touching the bottom. Label all parts of your system, including where the magnets or magnetic strips are located and how they are arranged (which way the poles are oriented).

3. Using ideas from the unit on magnetism, explain how your model will work.

4. Imagine that you've gone to Japan and you've been invited to ride in the control room of a maglev train. You're traveling at 300 miles per hour and one of the engineers reads a gauge that says one of the magnets under the train has cracked. Should you worry? Why or why not? [Use ideas from the magnetism unit to justify your answer.]

CQ 6-2. Should you worry?

A.YES
B.NO

5. A radio call reports that catastrophe was narrowly averted when a fire on the line 50 miles ahead was put out. The crew laughs about it and assures you not to worry, that you will make it to Osaka on time. What do you say to them? [Use ideas from the magnetism unit to justify your answer.]

CQ 6-3. Should you worry?

A.YES
B.NO

## Purpose

In the previous lessons you explored some magnetic effects and then went on to develop a model that explains these effects in terms of tiny entities within magnetic materials. You are also likely familiar with some other phenomena, usually associated with *static electricity*, like the 'static cling' by which clothes stick together when you remove them from a drier, or the 'shock' you receive when you walk across a carpet and then touch something. In this lesson, you will explore some static electric effects and compare these to the magnetic effects you already explored to see how magnetism and static electricity are similar and different.

> *What are some properties of interactions involving electrified objects, and how do they compare with interactions involving magnetic objects?*

## Predictions, Observations and Making Sense

### Part 1: What kinds of materials can be involved in static electric effects?

In a previous lesson you found that only certain materials could interact with a magnet. Will it be only these same materials that interact with electrified objects, or will different materials show static electric effects? What do you think?

---

**CQ 7-1: What kinds of materials do you think can be involved in static electric effects?**

A. All materials, both metals (copper, aluminum, iron, brass, etc.) and non-metals (plastic, wood, glass, etc.)
B. Only metals, but not non-metals
C. Only non-metals, but not metals
D. Only certain metals, not all metals
E. Only certain metals and non-metals, but not all of them

---

To find out, watch a movie (UM L7 Mov1), where the experimenter will first lay one piece of tape on the table (labeled B tape), and lay a second piece of tape on top of it (labeled T-tape). The two pieces of tape will then be held up by their ends and ripped apart. This process will 'electrify' each piece of tape.

Tape T on top of Tape B

Next, different objects will be brought near the T-tape and the B-tape and you should observe what happens. Is the tape attracted (A) to the object, repelled (R) from it, or does nothing happen (O)? Record your observations in the following table.

**Table I: Observations of Electrified Tapes near Objects (A, R or O)**

|  | Wooden strip | Iron nail | Plastic pen | Aluminum foil strip | Copper wire | Nickel strip | Finger |
|---|---|---|---|---|---|---|---|
| B-tape |  |  |  |  |  |  |  |
| T-tape |  |  |  |  |  |  |  |

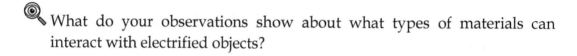 What do your observations show about what types of materials can interact with electrified objects?

How do these results compare with what types of materials can interact with magnetized objects?

*When Benjamin Franklin experimented with electrified objects, he imagined them as containing some type of electrical 'fluid' and so said they were 'charged' (as in 'charge [fill] your glasses for a toast') when describing them. While Franklin's use of 'charged' is probably different from the sense in which most people today think of it, we still use his terminology. Thus, from now on we will refer to electrified objects as being 'charged' with static electricity.*

## Part 2: How do electrically charged objects interact with each other?

In Part 1 you saw what happens when uncharged objects are brought near charged objects. But what would happen if the two charged tapes (B and T) were brought near each other?

Do you think they would behave like two magnets, which attract or repel depending on which ends/faces are brought close, or would they behave in a different manner? Explain your thinking.

---

**CQ 7-2:   If different ends/faces of two electrically charged tapes were brought close together, what do you think would happen?**

A. It would be like two magnets. If they attracted each other when two of the ends/faces were close to each other, they would then repel if one of the ends/faces were turned around.

B. It would not be like two magnets.  If two ends/faces attracted or repelled each other, they would do the same thing if one of the ends/faces were turned around.

C. They would not react to each other.

---

To find out, watch a movie (UM L7 Mov2).  In this movie, the experimenter will prepare two charged tapes as he did in the previous movie, bring each side of each tape (B-tape and T-tape) near each other, and then turn the tapes around.

What happened when the two non-sticky sides of the B and T tapes initially approached each other? Did they attract, repel, or was there no reaction?

What happened when one of the tapes was turned around, and the B and T tapes were again brought near each other?

What happened when the other tape was turned around so both sticky sides faced each other?

Do the results depend which sides are tested, or does the same thing always happen?

 How does this behavior of two charged tapes compare to the behavior of two magnetized nails you saw in previous lessons?

 In the magnetism lessons you concluded that a magnetized object is *two-ended*. Based on your observations from the movie, would you conclude that a charged object is *one-ended* or *two-ended*? How do you know?

## Part 3: How many types of charge are there?

You have seen that when peeling apart two tapes, each tape becomes charged with static electricity. But is there only one type of charge, or are there more than one and if so, how many are there?

 Imagine two pairs of tapes were each charged as shown previously (call them T1/B1 and T2/B2). If you then brought tapes T1 and T2 together, what do you think would happen?

---

**CQ 7-3: If the T1 and T2 tapes from two separate pairs of charged tapes were brought back toward each other, what do you think would happen?**

    A. They would attract each other.
    B. They would repel each other.
    C. They would not react to each other.

---

Watch a movie (UM L7 Mov3) of an experiment in which two pairs of B and T tapes are charged and then brought toward each other in various combinations.

Record the results of all the tests in Table II below. (Enter **A** for attract, **R** for repel, or **O** for no reaction.)

**Table II: Observations with Charged Tapes**

|     | B2  | T2  |
| --- | --- | --- |
| **B1** |     |     |
| **T1** |     |     |

 What do the results from these experiments with charged tapes suggest about the number of types of charge involved and how they interact with each other?

Finally, we will check whether the ideas you have developed about charges using the pairs of tapes also apply to objects charged by rubbing them together. Watch a movie (**UM L7 Mov4**) in which a balloon is rubbed against a person's hair and is brought back close to the hair again. Then the rubbed balloon is brought near charged T and B tapes.

 What happened when the rubbed balloon was brought back towards the hair?

 What does this observation suggest about the charges on the rubbed balloon and the rubbed hair? Are they the same or different?

 What happened when the rubbed balloon was brought near the B-tape? What happened when it was brought near the T-tape?

Based on these observations, does the rubbed balloon have the same charge as the T-tape or the B-tape? How do you know?

## Summarizing Questions

S1. Use evidence from this lesson to answer the following question.

> **CQ 7-4: How many types of charge are there and how do they interact?**
>
> A. There is only one type of charge. All charged objects attract each other.
> B. There is only one type of charge. All charged objects repel each other.
> C. There are two types of charge. Like charges repel and unlike charges attract.
> D. There are two types of charge. Like charges attract and unlike charges repel.

S2. Answer the following question based on your current understanding of what happens when objects are charged by rubbing or peeling.

> **CQ 7-5: What happens when two objects are charged by rubbing or peeling?**
>
> A. Both objects have the same type of charge.
> B. One object has only one type of charge. The other object has only the other type of charge.
> C. Both objects have both types of charge, but there are different amounts of each type on each object.

**Law of Electric Charges**

The evidence from the movies you observed in this lesson support what is known as the *Law of Electric Charges: There are two types of charge. Like charges repel and unlike charges attract.* This is similar in form to the Law of Magnetic Poles. However, as you concluded from the experiments in this lesson, although the forms of the two laws are similar, magnetized objects and charged objects behave differently, suggesting that the explanations (or models) for the two phenomena are different.

# Unit SE
# Developing a Model for Static Electricity

Soda–can + tinsel

Acrylic | Styrofoam

*Next Gen*

**Lecture-style Class**

# Unit SE: Developing a Model for Static Electricity
## Table of Contents

## Purpose and Materials Needed

In the previous unit you explored some magnetic effects and then went on to develop a model that explains these effects in terms of tiny entities within magnetic materials. You are also likely familiar with some other phenomena, usually associated with *static electricity*, like the 'static cling' by which clothes stick together when you remove them from a drier, or the 'shock' you receive when you walk across a carpet and then touch something. In this unit, you will develop another model to explain these effects associated with static electricity. To start, in this lesson you will observe some static electric effects and look for some patterns on which to base your initial model.

 *What are some properties of interactions involving electrified objects?*

For these investigations your team will need:

▸ Roll of sticky tape
▸ Pen or permanent marker
▸ A support, such as a ruler or long pencil
▸ An envelope containing several items

## Predictions, Observations and Making Sense

### Part 1: What kinds of materials can be involved in static electric effects?

In the previous unit you found that only certain materials could interact with a magnet. Will it be only these same materials that interact with electrified objects, or will different materials show static electric effects? What do you think?

---

**CQ 1-1: What kinds of materials do you think can be involved in static electric effects?**

A. All materials, both metals (copper, aluminum, iron, brass, etc.) and non-metals (plastic, wood, glass, etc.)
B. Only metals, but not non-metals
C. Only non-metals, but not metals
D. Only certain metals, not all metals
E. Only certain metals and non-metals, but not all of them

---

To find out, you will perform some experiments with electrified and non-electrified objects. You are no doubt aware that some objects can be electrified by rubbing them, but for these experiments you will use a different technique to electrify two pieces of sticky tape.

To begin, open the small envelope in your kit and lay out all the items (listed in Table I on the next page) on a desktop. Add two additional items that you will be testing.

*Read through the following steps first, and then go through them quickly, but carefully. Static electricity effects sometimes wear off quickly, so if you don't observe any types of interactions you might consider re-electrifying the tapes.* If you don't have the materials, watch the movie **USE L1 Mov1**.

Prepare two pieces of sticky tape, each about 4 inches long. Fold over about $1/2$ inch of both ends of both pieces of sticky tape. These ends will serve as 'handles' that will allow you to work with the tape without touching the sticky surfaces.

Place one of the pieces of tape on the desk in front of you, sticky side down. Using a pen or other permanent marker, label one of the handles on this piece B (for Bottom).

Now place a second piece of tape directly on top of the first, again sticky side down. Label this piece T (for Top).

Tape T on top of Tape B

Rub you finger over the two pieces to make sure they are firmly stuck together. (The bottom piece will also be stuck to the table, but that is not important.)

**One member of your group** should slowly peel both pieces of tape, still stuck together, from the table. (If the two pieces of tape become separated press them firmly together again.)

*Holding a handle on each piece of tape in each hand, quickly rip them apart. Keep your two hands far apart so the tapes do not touch.* [Ripping the tapes apart should electrify each of them.]

To find out how the various materials in your envelope interact with the electrified tapes, *other members of your group should slowly bring each item close to each of the two tapes in turn. Do this quickly.* As soon as any reaction from the tape is observed, pull the object away again. Try not to let the tape touch any of the objects. Without the materials you should watch the movie [USE L1 Mov2].

For each item, record in the table whether the tape is attracted (A) to it, repelled (R) from it, or there is no effect (O). Add two other items of your own choice to the table and test them. Finally, bring the tip of your finger close to each tape to see if there is any reaction.

### Table I: Observations of Electrified Tapes near Objects (A, R or O)

|  | Wooden strip | Iron nail | Plastic pen/ruler | Aluminum foil strip | Copper wire | Nickel strip | Paper clip |  | Finger |
|---|---|---|---|---|---|---|---|---|---|
| T-tape |  |  |  |  |  |  |  |  |  |
| B-tape |  |  |  |  |  |  |  |  |  |

What do your observations show about what types of materials can interact with electrified objects?

You can discard the two tapes. Your instructor will review the observations in the Table and your conclusions to ensure that everyone agrees.

*When Benjamin Franklin experimented with electrified objects, he imagined them as containing some type of electrical 'fluid' and so said they were 'charged' (as in 'charge [fill] your glasses for a toast') when describing them. While Franklin's use of 'charged' is probably different from the sense in which most people today think of it, we still use his terminology. Thus, from now on we will refer to electrified objects as being 'charged' with static electricity.*

## Part 2: How do electrically charged objects interact with each other?

In Part 1 you saw what happens when uncharged objects are brought near charged objects. But what would happen if two charged objects were brought near each other?

? Do you think they would behave like two magnets, which attract or repel depending on which ends/faces are brought close, or would they behave in a different manner? Explain your thinking.

---

**CQ 1-2: If different ends/faces of two electrically charged objects were brought close together, what do you think would happen?**

A. It would be like two magnets. If they attracted each other when two of the ends/faces were close to each other, they would then repel if one of the ends/faces were turned around.
B. It would not be like two magnets. If two ends/faces attracted or repelled each other, they would do the same thing if one of the ends/faces were turned around.
C. They would not react to each other.

---

Two different experiments will help you check your thinking.

First, watch a movie (USE L1 Mov3) of an experiment involving two plastic coffee stirrers. So that you can distinguish the ends, one end of each stirrer will have a small piece of tape attached to it. One of the stirrers will be charged by rubbing it all over with wool, and then placed on a floating disk.

The second stirrer will be charged in the same manner, and then both ends of it will be brought close to both ends of the floating charged stirrer.

 Does what happens depend on which ends of the stirrers are tested, or does the same thing always happen regardless of the ends used?

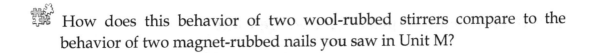 How does this behavior of two wool-rubbed stirrers compare to the behavior of two magnet-rubbed nails you saw in Unit M?

The next experiment you will perform yourself. (If you do not have the materials, then watch **USE L1 Mov4**.) Prepare a new pair of charged B and T tapes just as you did in Part 1. After ripping the B and T tapes apart, slowly bring them toward each other. As soon as you see any reaction, move them apart again. *It is important not to let the tapes touch each other!* (If they do, you should go through the whole charging process again!)

 What happens as the B and T tapes approach each other? Do they attract, repel, or is there no reaction?

**Turn one of the tapes around** so its opposite side faces the other tape, and bring the two tapes together again.

Do the results depend which ends/faces are tested, or does the same thing always happen?

In Unit M, you investigated what materials interact with a magnet and also whether magnetized objects are one-ended or two-ended.

Based on your observations in this lesson, what can you conclude: are charged objects one-ended or two-ended?

 When compared with the results of your investigations in Unit M, do observations in this lesson suggest that the static electric and magnetic interactions are the same or different? Explain your reasoning.

## Part 3: How many types of charge are there?

You have seen that during rubbing with wool, and the peeling apart of two tapes, objects involved become charged with static electricity. But is there only one type of charge, or are there more than one and if so, how many are there?

 Suppose you prepared two pairs of charged tapes (call them T1/B1 and T2/B2) and brought tapes T1 and T2 together. What do you think would happen and why?

---

**CQ 1-3: If the T1 and T2 tapes from two separate pairs of charged tapes were brought back toward each other, what do you think would happen?**

A. They would attract each other.
B. They would repel each other.
C. They would not react to each other.

---

Either perform the following experiment with the materials or watch a movie (**USE L1 Mov5**) of the experiment. Prepare two pairs of B and T tapes so they are charged and label them B1, T1, B2, and T2. Then bring them toward each other in various combinations, as suggested in the following table.

---

Record the results of all the tests in Table II below. (Enter **A** for attract, **R** for repel, or **O** for no reaction.)

**Table II: Observations with Charged Tapes**

|  | B2 | T2 |
|---|---|---|
| B1 |  |  |
| T1 |  |  |

 What do the results from these experiments with charged tapes suggest about the number of types of charge involved and how they interact with each other?

Finally, we will check whether the ideas you have developed about charges using the pairs of tapes also apply to objects charged by rubbing them together.

Watch a movie (USE L1 Mov6) of an experiment in which a Styrofoam plate and an acrylic sheet (a type of clear plastic) are rubbed together and each brought toward a pair of charged B and T tapes.

 Describe how both tapes behave when the rubbed Styrofoam plate is brought near.

 Do these results suggest that the rubbed plate has the same type of charge as the B tape, the T tape, or some different type of charge?

Describe how both tapes behave when the rubbed acrylic sheet is brought near.

 Do these results suggest that the rubbed acrylic sheet has the same type of charge as the B tape, the T tape, or some different type of charge?

Next, watch a movie (USE L1 Mov7) that shows a rubber balloon being rubbed against a person's hair. Then the charged balloon is brought close to T and B tapes.

 Describe how both tapes behave when the hair-rubbed balloon is brought near.

 Do these results suggest that the hair-rubbed balloon has the same type of charge as the B tape, the T tape, or some different type of charge?

## Summarizing Questions

S1. Use evidence from this lesson to answer the following question.

---

**CQ 1-4: How many types of charge are there and how do they interact?**

A. There is only one type of charge. All charged objects attract each other.
B. There is only one type of charge. All charged objects repel each other.
C. There are two types of charge. Like charges repel and unlike charges attract.
D. There are two types of charge. Like charges attract and unlike charges repel.

---

**S2.** Suppose you and your neighbors both rubbed a Styrofoam plate with an acrylic sheet and then brought the two plates together. What do you think would happen and why? What about if you brought your charged plate close to their charged acrylic sheet?

To get some feedback, watch the movie USE L1 Mov8, which shows what happens when the two Styrofoam plates are brought together.

What actually happens?

**S3.** Answer the following question based on your current understanding of what happens when objects are charged by rubbing or peeling.

---

**CQ 1-5: What happens when two objects are charged by rubbing or peeling?**
   A. Both objects have the same type of charge.
   B. One object has only one type of charge. The other object has only the other type of charge.
   C. Both objects have both types of charge, but there are different amounts of each type on each object.

---

## Purpose

In the previous unit, you developed and tested a model for magnetism that can account for what happens when a nail is rubbed with a magnet. In this lesson, you will begin the process of developing a *model for static electricity* that can account for how objects become charged with static electricity when they are rubbed together (or tapes pulled apart) and why they behave as they do when interacting with other objects, both charged and uncharged.

*Note: While it would be good to obtain your evidence from experiments you do yourself, it is notoriously difficult to obtain consistent results with static electricity experiments in humid conditions like a classroom full of people. (You will consider why this might be in a later lesson.) Therefore, from now on you will mostly be making observations of experiments from videos made under controlled conditions.*

> **How can you construct a model of static electricity and use it to explain your observations?**

## Predictions, Observations and Making Sense

### Part 1: What is your initial model for static electricity?

You know from the previous lesson that there seems to be two types of electric charge, just as there are two types of magnetic poles. However, you also saw that charged objects are *one-ended* (both sides or ends behave in the same way), whereas magnetized objects are *two-ended*. In representing magnetic materials we used north (N) and south (S) symbols. However, because the two types of interaction are different in some way, we should use different symbols when representing charged materials. To make this distinction, we suggest you use positive (+) and negative (–) symbols in your models.

Using this convention, from the previous extension activity you concluded that when a Styrofoam plate is rubbed with an acrylic sheet, the acrylic sheet becomes positively (+) charged and the Styrofoam plate becomes negatively (–) charged.

 Use the two drawings of the plate and sheet below to show your group's thinking, representing their states before and after they were charged. This represents your group's initial *model*.

**Your group's initial model for rubbing two materials together:**

| Before rubbing together | After rubbing together |
|---|---|
| Styrofoam plate　　　Acrylic sheet | Styrofoam plate　　　Acrylic sheet |

 Describe your group's initial model in words, in particular how the "after rubbing" picture differs from the "before rubbing" picture. What do you think happens to the entities (if anything) while the plate and sheet are rubbed together?

 Use your model to briefly explain the observation that *the Styrofoam and acrylic become oppositely charged when rubbed together, and that each of them is 'one-ended'*.

**CQ 2-1: Which of the following best describes your initial model for what happens when the acrylic and Styrofoam are charged by rubbing them together?**

A. Neither of the objects have any charged entities before rubbing together. During the rubbing, + charges are created on the acrylic, and – charges are created on the Styrofoam.

B. Before rubbing, both objects have equal numbers of + and – charges. During rubbing, charges are transferred so that the acrylic ends up with all the + charges and the Styrofoam ends up with all the – charges.

C. Before rubbing, both objects have equal numbers of + and – charges. During rubbing, some charges are transferred so that the acrylic ends up with more + charges than – charges, and the Styrofoam ends up with more – charges than + charges.

D. Before rubbing, both objects have equal numbers of + and – charges. During rubbing, extra + charges are created on the acrylic and extra – charges are created on the Styrofoam.

In the previous extension activity, you were also introduced to a simulation that represents positive charge with red coloring and negative charge with blue coloring. Watch a brief movie (USE L2 Mov1) that simulates the acrylic sheet and Styrofoam being rubbed together. Notice the rubbed acrylic surface is colored red (+ charged) and the rubbed Styrofoam surface is colored blue (- charged).

## Part 2: Touching charged and uncharged objects together

The experiments you will consider shortly use a device called an electroscope, made from an empty metal soda can taped to an upturned Styrofoam cup. Some loose strands of tinsel (which are effectively thin strips of metal) are hung from the ring-pull tab of the can so that the ends are free to move.

Watch a movie (USE L2 Mov2) of an experiment in which a Styrofoam plate and acrylic sheet are first charged by rubbing them together. The + charged acrylic sheet then gently touches the tinsel on the electroscope and is pulled away again (they are **not** rubbed together). After this is done, the strands of tinsel are hanging in a **more 'spread out'** arrangement than before. Below are still frames from the movie.

*Before: tinsel strands are close together*   *After: tinsel strands are more spread out*

 After the + charged acrylic sheet touches the tinsel and is removed, do you think the tinsel is itself charged or not, and, if so, what type of charge does it have: the same as the acrylic sheet (+) or the opposite (-)? On the following diagrams, draw what +/– charged entities you think are inside or on the surface of the tinsel (if any), end of the soda can, and acrylic sheet before and after they have been in contact. Discuss your thinking with your group.

 After the + charged acrylic touches the tinsel and is removed, does your model suggest the tinsel is now uncharged, + charged, or – charged?

How do your diagrams account for the observation that the strands of tinsel are hanging in a more 'spread out' arrangement after contact than before? (*Assume that the charged acrylic is too far away to directly affect the tinsel at these points in time.*)

You can check your ideas by making a prediction that can be tested. After the tinsel has touched the charged acrylic sheet, suppose first the + charged acrylic sheet and then the – charged Styrofoam plate were brought close to the tinsel again, **but not allowed to touch it.**

---

**CQ 2-2:  According to your model above, after the tinsel has touched the charged acrylic sheet, how would it react to the + charged acrylic and - charged Styrofoam?**

    A.  Attracted to the acrylic and repelled by the Styrofoam.
    B.  Attracted to both the acrylic and the Styrofoam.
    C.  Repelled by the acrylic and attracted to the Styrofoam.
    D.  Repelled by both the acrylic and the Styrofoam.

---

Briefly explain your reasoning.

To get feedback, watch a movie (USE L2 Mov3) of the experiment being performed.

 Describe how the tinsel reacts (attracts, repels, no effect) to the:

    + charged acrylic sheet.

    – charged Styrofoam plate.

 Based on your observations, what can you conclude about the charge state of the tinsel strands after they had touched the charged acrylic sheet? Did they have a positive (+) charge, a negative (-) charge, or no charge? How do you know?

Next, watch a movie (USE L2 Mov4) from the simulation, representing what happens when the + charged acrylic touches the tinsel on the soda can. At the beginning of the movie, none of the objects are charged, but as it plays, charged areas will be represented by red (+) or blue (–) colors.

Based on your observations from the experiment and the simulation, discuss with your group whether your model needs to be revised. If so, re-draw it below. Remember to show what +/- charges, if any, are on the surface or inside the tinsel, end of soda can, and charged acrylic both before and after the acrylic touches the tinsel.

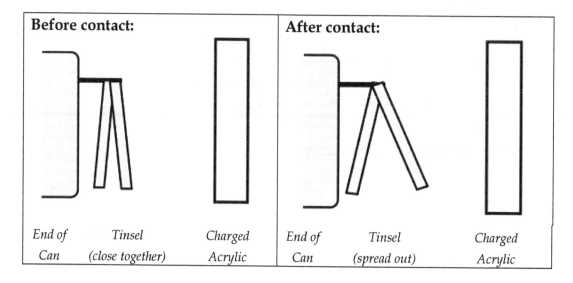

| Before contact: | | | After contact: | | |
|---|---|---|---|---|---|
| End of | Tinsel | Charged | End of | Tinsel | Charged |
| Can | (close together) | Acrylic | Can | (spread out) | Acrylic |

Explain, in terms of the charged entitites involved, what you think happened when the tinsel touched the charged acrylic sheet.

*Note: The behavior of the tinsel on an electroscope will serve as a tool in further experiments. If the tinsel is itself uncharged it will not react to an uncharged object, but it will be attracted toward any charged object, regardless of whether it is positively (+) or negatively (–) charged. (You know*

*that there is always an attraction between charged and uncharged objects.)*
*Thus we can use it to check if an object is charged or not. If the tinsel*
*becomes spread out, we know it is now charged and we can test what type of*
*charge it has by using charged acrylic and Styrofoam.*

## Part 3: What happens when a charged object is touched all over with an uncharged object?

Watch a movie (USE L2 Mov5) in which an experimenter rubs a plastic coffee stirrer with wool and then touches it all over with his fingers. To check whether the stirrer is charged or not at various points in the process, it will be brought close to the **uncharged tinsel** strands on a soda can electroscope.

Was the stirrer charged before it was rubbed with wool? What about after? How do you know?

Explain, in terms of the +/− charged entities involved in your model, what you think happened when the plastic stirrer was rubbed with the wool.

Now consider what happened when the experimenter touched the stirrer all over with his fingers.

Was the stirrer still charged after this was done? How do you know?

Explain, in terms of the +/− charged entitites involved in your model, what you think happened when the experimenter touched the plastic stirrer with his fingers.

CQ 2-3: Now imagine that after charging the stirrer with the wool, the experimenter immersed the stirrer in water and then removed it. If he brought the wet stirrer near the uncharged tinsel, what do you predict would happen?

A. The tinsel would be attracted to the wet stirrer.
B. The tinsel would be repelled from the wet stirrer.
C. The tinsel would not react to the wet stirrer.

Why do you think so?

Watch a movie (USE L2 Mov6) of what actually happens.

What happened when the wet stirrer was brought near the tinsel?

Was the stirrer charged <u>after</u> it was immersed in water? How do you know?

If this result is not in agreement with your prediction, describe how your model might explain it in terms of the charged entities involved.

How might this result help explain why it is difficult to do static electricity experiments when there is a lot of humidity in the atmosphere?

## Summarizing Questions

**S1.** You already know that **two uncharged objects** can be charged by rubbing them together (or peeling tapes apart).

---

**CQ 2-4:** What do your observations in this lesson suggest happens when an uncharged object touches a second object that is already charged?

    A. The uncharged object becomes charged in the same way as the second object.

    B. The uncharged object becomes charged in the opposite way as the second object.

    C. The uncharged object remains uncharged.

---

**S2.** Do your observations suggest that in your model you should regard the charged entities responsible for giving an object its overall charge as being inside the body of the object or on its surface? What evidence supports your answer?

## Purpose

In the previous lesson you developed your initial model to account for static electric phenomena. It is common for most groups to have similar models for charged objects, associating arrangements of positively (+) and negatively (–) charged entities with them. However, there is often more variation in the model representations of uncharged objects (such as the acrylic sheet and Styrofoam plate before they were rubbed together), with some showing no entities, some showing neutral (uncharged) entities, and some showing equal numbers of + and – charged entities. The key question for this lesson is:

 *What is an appropriate way to represent uncharged objects in your model for static electricity?*

## Predictions, Observations and Making Sense

### Part 1: Bringing a charged object close to the electroscope

In the previous lesson you were introduced to a device called an electroscope, made from a soda can and some tinsel (thin metal strips). Suppose you had such a soda can electroscope that was **uncharged**. According to your current model, how would you represent this uncharged eleclectroscope?

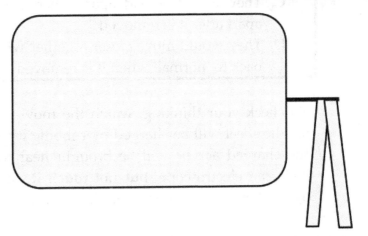

? Use this diagram to show your thinking, drawing whatever entities (if any) you think necessary on both the can and the tinsel.

?🧑 How does your diagram indicate that the soda can and tinsel are both uncharged? What evidence (if any) do you have to support this representation?

## Part 2: Bringing a positively (+) charged object close to the uncharged electroscope

?🧑 Suppose you rubbed an acrylic sheet and a Styrofoam plate together to charge them, and then brought the positively (+) charged acrylic sheet close to (**but not touching**) the base of the uncharged electroscope you represented in Part 1. Do you think either the soda-can or the tinsel would become electrically charged when this is done?

CQ 3-1: **If the charged acrylic sheet was brought close to the base of the can and then removed again (without touching the can), how do you think the tinsel strands at the other end of the can would behave?**

A. They would not react in any way.
B. They would spread apart when the acrylic is near but then go back to 'normal' when it is removed.
C. They would spread apart when the acrylic is near and stay spread apart after it is removed.
D. They would move closer together when the acrylic is near but then go back to 'normal' when it is removed.

To check your thinking, watch the movie USE L3 Mov1. In this movie an acrylic sheet will be charged by rubbing it with a Styrofoam plate. After this, the charged acrylic will be brought near to the base end of an uncharged soda-can electroscope, **but not touch it**, and then be moved further away again. This will be done a couple of times.

When the charged acryclic sheet is brought close to the other end of the soda can, does the tinsel become more spread out, more clumped together, or does it not show any reaction? What happens when the acrylic sheet is removed again?

Does this evidence support the conclusion that the <u>tinsel</u> is now *charged* or that it is *uncharged* when the charged acrylic is held nearby?

Work with your group to try and explain this behavior using your model, revising it if necessary.

Use the diagrams below to show how your current model now represents the objects involved (soda can, tinsel, and acrylic) before the charged acrylic is brought close, while it is close (with the tinsel spread out), and after it has been removed again.

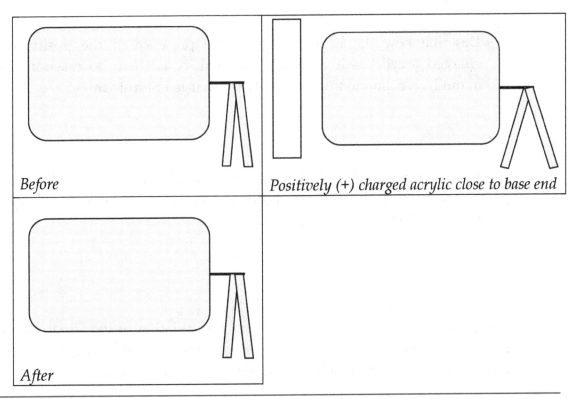

Before

*Positively (+) charged acrylic close to base end*

After

Explain how your model accounts for the behavior of the tinsel in terms of any entities involved.

You have now seen that when the positively (+) charged acrylic sheet is held close to the base end of the soda can electroscope, the tinsel at the other end becomes more spread out. From this you can infer that while the acrylic sheet is held in this position, the tinsel becomes charged, but was it positive (+) or negative (–)? Also, did the base end of the can become charged or not, and what happened to the charge on the acrylic?

To gather evidence to help address these questions, watch a movie (**USE L3 Mov2**). It shows the experimenter preparing two sets of charged acrylic and Styrofoam. He first holds one of the positively charged (+) acrylic sheets close to the base end of the uncharged electroscope and the tinsel spreads out (as it did in the previous movie). Keeping the first positively (+) charged acrylic sheet close to the base end of the electroscope, he then brings the other positively (+) charged acrylic sheet close to the tinsel, followed by one of negatively (–) charged Styrofoam plates.

Describe how the tinsel reacts to the presence of the positively (+) charged acrylic. Is it attracted, repelled, or is there no reaction? What about its reaction to the negatively (–) charged Styrofoam?

When the positively (+) charged acrylic was held close to the base end of the uncharged electroscope, did the tinsel have a positive (+) or negative (–) charge? How do you know?

Next, watch a movie (**USE L3 Mov3**) of a simulation of the situation where the acrylic and Styrofoam are rubbed together and the charged acrylic is brought near (without touching) the base end of the soda can.

🔍 According to the simulation, when the positively (+) charged acrylic is brought close to one end of the simulator electroscope, does the tinsel at the other end become positively (+) or negatively (–) charged, or does it remain uncharged? How do you know?

🔍 While the positively (+) charged acrylic is held close to one side of the simulator electroscope, does that side of the electroscope (closest to the acrylic) become positively (+) or negatively (–) charged, or does it remain uncharged? How do you know?

🔍 After the positively (+) charged acrylic is moved away from the simulator electroscope, what happens to the charge state of the tinsel and the other end? Do they remain charged or do they become uncharged again? How do you know?

Based on your observations of the experiments and the simulation, your group should modify its model, if needed, to explain what happens when the positively (+) charged acrylic is brought near the base end of the electroscope.

Before

Positively (+) charged acrylic close to base end

After

Briefly explain how the proximity of the positively (+) charged acrylic at the base end results in the tinsel end of the electroscope acquiring an an overall positive (+) charge and the base end an overall negative (–) charge.

As an extension activity to this lesson, you will explore what happens when a negatively (–) charged object is brought close to the uncharged electroscope.

## Summarizing Questions

**S1.** Answer the following question based on the evidence you obtained during this lesson.

> **CQ 3-2:** Which of the following ideas about uncharged objects do you think it would it be most appropriate to include in your model?
>
> A. They have no electric entities associated with them. When such objects are involved in static electric interactions, + and – charged entities are created.
> B. They have neutral (uncharged) electric entities associate with them. When such objects are involved in static electric interactions, these neutral entities are changed into either + or – charged entities.
> C. They have equal numbers of + and – charged entities associated with them. When such objects are involved in static electric interactions, at least some of these entities move around.

**S2.** Use your model to explain why the tinsel on an uncharged electroscope goes back to hanging normally when a charged object is moved away from the other end. (You saw this happening at the end of the simulation movie **USE L3 Mov3**.)

## Purpose

You are currently developing a model for static electricity that involves the movement of +/– charged entities within and/or between objects. In this lesson, you will continue this development to account for how different materials behave when involved in static electricity effects.

 LESSON

> *How can you refine your model to account for the behavior of metals and non-metals?*

## Predictions, Observations and Making Sense

<u>Part 1</u>: **Can you charge an object without touching it directly?**

In the previous lessons you saw that when some tinsel strands come into contact with a charged object, the tinsel itself becomes charged. In this lesson we will use two electroscopes, one made with a metal soda can as you saw in the previous lessons, and the second made with a plastic water bottle. Both are initially **<u>uncharged</u>**.

To begin, watch a movie (USE L4 Mov1) of an experiment in which a positively (+) charged acrylic sheet is brought into **contact** with the **base end** of the soda can and water bottle on the uncharged electroscopes (the ends opposite the tinsel) for a few seconds, and then removed.

🔍 Describe what happens to the tinsel on each electroscope when this is done.

When the + charged acrylic sheet was touched to both electroscopes, did the tinsel strands at the other end of the electroscopes became charged or not? How do you know?

?⚑ Use the diagrams below to show your thinking about the +/– charged entities on the **charged acrylic sheet, the soda can, water bottle, and the tinsel**, both before and after they have been in contact.

Explain, in terms of the +/− charged entities involved, what you think happened when the acrylic sheet was touched to the base of both electroscopes and why the tinsel behaved as it did.

Participate in the class vote and discussion about this question.

---

**CQ 4-1: According to your diagrams, after the positively (+) charged acrylic sheet was in contact with the base of the soda can and the water bottle, how were the tinsel strands at the other end of each electroscope charged, if at all?**

    A. The tinsel on both was uncharged.

    B. The tinsel on the soda can was positively (+) charged. The tinsel on the water bottle was uncharged.

    C. The tinsel on the soda can was negatively (−) charged. The tinsel on the water bottle was uncharged.

    D. The tinsel on both was negatively (−) charged.

    E. The tinsel on both was positively (+) charged.

---

Now consider how your response to CQ 4-1 could be checked by making some predictions.

 If the tinsel on both electroscopes was charged according to your chosen response, how would it behave when a + charged acrylic sheet and a − charged Styrofoam plate were brought near to it? Fill in the prediction Table and briefly discuss your reasoning with your group.

**Prediction Table: What do you think would happen to the tinsel if the ... were brought near the ...? Choose _A_ttract, _R_epel or n_O_thing.**

| Brought near the tinsel | Tinsel on **soda-can** electroscope | Tinsel on **water-bottle** electroscope |
|---|---|---|
| Positively (+) charged acrylic | | |
| Negatively (−) charged Styrofoam | | |

Watch a movie (USE L4 Mov2) where the base end of the soda can and water bottle electroscopes were touched by the + charged acrylic sheet (not shown in movie), and then a charged acrylic sheet and charged Styrofoam plate are separately brought close to (but not touching) the tinsel strands on both electroscopes.

 Fill in your observations in the Table.

**Observation Table: What actually happened to the tinsel when the ... were brought near the ...? Choose _A_ttract, _R_epel or n_O_thing.**

|  | Tinsel on **soda-can** electroscope | Tinsel on **water-bottle** electroscope |
|---|---|---|
| Positively (+) charged acrylic |  |  |
| Negatively (−) charged Styrofoam |  |  |

 After the acrylic sheet was in contact with the base of the metal soda can, were the tinsel strands positively (+) or negatively (−) charged, or were they still uncharged? How do you know?

 After the acrylic sheet was in contact with the base of the plastic water bottle, were the tinsel strands positively (+) or negatively (−) charged, or were they still uncharged? How do you know?

If these outcomes do not agree with your predictions, discuss with your group how you could modify your thinking about the mobility of the charged entities in different materials to account for it.

 Describe your current thinking about why the metal soda can and the plastic soda bottle produced different results in these experiments.

## Part 2: How can charged materials be discharged?

You have seen how uncharged objects can become charged, either by rubbing them together (or peeling apart, in the case of the tapes) or by touching them with another object that is already charged. Now we will consider how we can turn a charged object into an uncharged object, a process called *discharging*.

Suppose you have a soda-can electroscope and a water-bottle electroscope. You charge the tinsel strands on both by touching them directly with a positively (+) charged acrylic sheet. You have already seen that this would cause the tinsel strands to themselves become positively (+) charged and hang in a more spread out pattern than before they were touched.

 Discuss with your group what you think would happen if you touched the **non-tinsel end** (the base of the can or bottle) with your finger (being careful not to touch the tinsel itself)? Why do you think so?

Participate in the class vote and discussion.

---

**CQ 4-2: What would happen if you touched the non-tinsel end of a positively (+) charged soda-can and water bottle electroscope?**
  A. Both electroscopes would discharge.
  B. Only the soda-can electroscope would discharge.
  C. Only the water-bottle electroscope would discharge.
  D. Neither electroscope would discharge.

---

Watch a movie (USE L4 Mov3) of the demonstation being performed. The tinsel on both electroscopes will be charged by allowing the strands to touch a positively (+) charged acrylic sheet. The demonstrator will then touch a finger to the non-tinsel end on both electroscopes. Watch the behavior of the tinsel when this is done. At the end, the demonstrator will allow the tinsel to touch some fingers directly.

 Which of the electroscopes could be discharged by touching the non-tinsel end—only the water bottle, only the soda can, or both? Explain why you think this is in terms of the behavior of the +/− charged entities in the different materials involved.

Why do you think the tinsel on the water-bottle electroscope could be discharged by touching it directly with some fingers, but touching the bottle itself did not work?

Recall that the outer surface of the tinsel strands is a thin layer of metal. Now let's consider how we could discharge an object that has no metal anywhere on it. You know that, when rubbed together, the rubbed surface of an acrylic sheet becomes positively (+) charged and the rubbed surface of a Styrofoam plate becomes negatively (−) charged.

If you wanted to discharge these two objects again, do you think it would be sufficient to touch each of them at **only one point** on the charged surface, or would it be better to touch **as much of the rubbed surface as possible**? Explain your thinking in terms of your ideas about the behavior of the +/− charged entities in these non-metallic materials.

Watch a movie (USE L4 Mov4) of both these ideas being tested. Whether the materials remain charged or not will be tested for using an **uncharged** soda-can electroscope. (Recall that there is always an attraction between a charged and an uncharged object.)

What happened? Did touching either the charged acrylic or charged Styrofoam at **one point** discharge them, or did you need to **touch all over** rub their rubbed surfaces? If the result does not agree with your prediction, discuss with your group how you could change your thinking about the behavior of charged and uncharged objects.

Does the result does agree with your prediction? If not, discuss with your group how you could change your model (in terms of the behavior of charged entities in non-metals) to account for it.

In a previous lesson you saw a plastic stirrer being charged by being rubbed with wool and then touched all over with the fingers. After being touched, the stirrer was no longer charged. (If you need a reminder, watch the movie (USE L4 Mov5) again.]

 Assuming the rubbed plastic stirrer was negatively (–) charged, how can your model explain this result in terms of the behavior of the +/– charged entities involved?

## Summarizing Questions

S1: As a result of the evidence you have seen in this lesson, you may have felt it necessary to revise your model so that it can account for the difference between how metals and non-metals behave when involved in static electric effects.

> **CQ 4-3: Which of the following best accounts for the difference between how metals and non-metals behave when involved in static electricity effects?**
> A. At least some of the charged entities can move around in non-metals, but not in metals.
> B. At least some of the charged entities can move around in metals, but not in non-metals.
> C. The charged entities in metals and non-metals are different and do not interact with each other.

**S2:** If you were to hold a brass rod in your hand and try to charge it by rubbing it with nylon, it would not work. However, if you were to wear thick rubber gloves, the brass rod would become charged. Briefly explain why this is.

**S3:** At this stage, your model probably accounts for an object being charged by assuming that it has more of one type of charge (+ or –) than the other.

---

**CQ 4-4:** Do the observations you have made so far in this unit suggest that it would be better to regard the excess of one type of charged entity as lying on the surface of an object, or deep within the body of the object? Why do you think so?
  A. The excess of one type of charged entity lies on the surface.
  B. The excess of one type of charged entity lies deep within the body of the object.
  C. At this time, there is no evidence to decide.

---

**S4:** In this lesson you saw that when the base end of an uncharged soda-can electroscope was **touched** with a positively (+) charged acrylic sheet, the tinsel at the other end also became positively (+) charged. Use the diagrams below to show how your current model can account for this in terms of the +/– charged entities involved.

| Before contact: | After contact: |

## Conductors and insulators

Scientists refer to materials in which at least some charged entities can move around relatively freely as *conductors*. Materials for which none of the charged entities are free to move around are called *insulators*.

## Purpose and Key Question

By now the class has likely reached consensus on a model of static electricity that should explain all the observations that have been made thus far. We refer to this model as the *charges in materials model*, and its basic **assumptions** are listed here. (1) Inside all objects there are two types of tiny charged entities, which we label + and −. The + charged entities are the protons in the nucleus of the atoms in the material and they cannot be easily removed or added to a material, or moved around. The − charged entities are the electrons that orbit around the nucleus and some of these can be removed or added to a material, and can move around to some degree. (2) In an uncharged material there are an equal number of + and − charges. An object is given an overall − charge when extra − charges are added to it. An object is given an overall + charge when some of its − charges are removed. The excess charges (+ or −) are on the surface of the material. (3) In metallic materials, some − charges are free to move throughout the body of the material. In non-metals, the − charges are not free to move through the material but stay attached to a particular atom. However, while staying attached to that atom they can be moved slightly with respect to the + charges in the nucleus.

In this lesson we will apply this model to explain some new observations.

 *How can you use the charges in materials model of static electricity to explain some phenomena?*

## Predictions, Observations and Making Sense

### Part 1: Can a charged object pick up small-uncharged objects?

You have seen that when a rubber balloon is rubbed on wool (or hair), it becomes negatively (−) charged. Suppose you rubbed a balloon on your hair then held it first above a pile of small pieces of aluminum foil (metal), and then above a pile of small pieces of paper (non-metal). Do you think the balloon would attract any of the pieces and so pick them up?

**CQ 5-1: If you hold a negatively (−) charged balloon above some small pieces of aluminum and paper, what do you think would happen?**
  A. The balloon would not pick up anything.
  B. The balloon would pick up some aluminum pieces, but no paper.
  C. The balloon would pick up some paper pieces, but no aluminum.
  D. The balloon would pick up both some paper and some aluminum pieces.

Why do you think so?

Watch a movie (USE L5 Mov) so you can test your prediction.

Which pieces does the balloon pick up: neither, only one type, or both?

Now use the model of charges in materials to explain this result. First use the diagrams below (which are not to scale) to show the +/− charges on the balloon and one of the uncharged **aluminum** pieces both when the negatively (−) charged balloon is far away and when it is closer.

Explain what happened to the +/− charged entities in the aluminum piece when the negatively (−) charged balloon was brought close.

 How does the arrangement of +/− entities in the aluminum piece explain why it is attracted to the balloon?

Now use the diagrams below to show the +/− charges on the balloon and one of the uncharged paper pieces both when the negatively (−) charged balloon is far away and then closer.

 Explain what happened to the +/− charged entities in the paper piece when the negatively (−) charged balloon was brought close.

How does the arrangement of +/− entities in the paper piece explain why it is attracted to the negatively (−) charged balloon?

## Part 2: How can you explain why clothes stick together in a dryer?

A student doing her laundry takes wet clothes from a washing machine and puts them in the dryer. When they are dry she takes them out and finds a pair of cotton socks stuck to a polyester shirt because of 'static cling'. Wondering what has happened to cause this, she does a quick experiment using a balloon hanging from string (left over from the previous night's party!). She rubs the balloon on her hair and then lets it hang freely from the string. When she brings the clothes near to the balloon, she finds it is attracted to the cotton socks but repelled by the polyester shirt. However, she finds that the cotton socks repel each other.

---

**CQ 5-2: What type of charge (+ or −) does the polyester shirt have, or is it uncharged?**
  A. The polyester shirt is + charged.
  B. The polyester shirt is − charged.
  C. The polyester shirt is uncharged.

---

How do you know?

---

**CQ 5-3: What type of charge (+ or −) do the cotton socks have, or are they uncharged?**
  A. The cotton socks are both + charged.
  B. The cotton socks are both − charged.
  C. One cotton sock is + charged; the other is − charged.
  D. The cotton socks are both uncharged.

---

How do you know?

Use the charges in materials model to explain what happened to the cotton socks and polyester shirt during drying. Draw + and – entities on the diagrams below.

Explain what happens to the cotton socks and polyester shirt during drying.

When the student checked on her laundry halfway through the drying cycle, it was still slightly damp, but there was also no 'static cling' evident. Why do you think this was?

 To reduce 'static cling', you can put a 'dryer sheet' in the dryer with your laundry. These sheets coat the fibers of all your clothes with the same waxy substance as it tumbles with them. How might this substance work to reduce the 'static cling'?